List of Tunes

A Note To Teachers

Dear colleagues,
I left it up to you to decide which fingers to use in each tune. *Non Legato* would be the best articulation.

ISBN 978-0-9931316-0-8

Published by EVC Music Publications

MY NAME IS _____I AM _____YEARS OLD, DATE_____

LEFT HAND   RIGHT HAND

Trace your hands and add numbers to your fingers, remember that your thumb is number 1.

Map of London (almost)

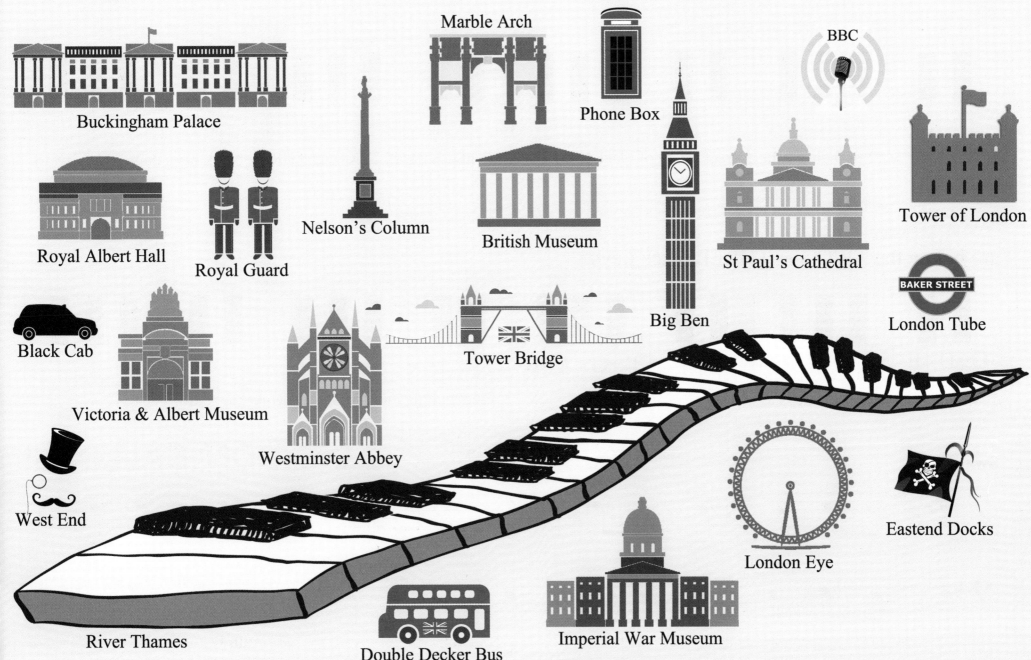

Buckingham Palace

Marble Arch

Phone Box

BBC

Tower of London

Royal Albert Hall

Royal Guard

Nelson's Column

British Museum

Big Ben

St Paul's Cathedral

London Tube

Black Cab

Victoria & Albert Museum

Westminster Abbey

Tower Bridge

London Eye

Eastend Docks

West End

River Thames

Double Decker Bus

Imperial War Museum

BLACK KEYS

are arranged in groups of TWO and THREE.

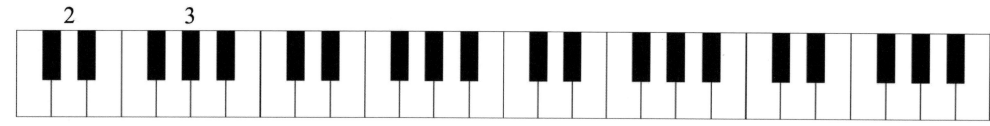

1. Write number 2 or 3 above the correct group of black keys.　　　2. Find groups of TWO and THREE black keys on your keyboard.

WHITE KEYS

are below the TWO and THREE black keys.

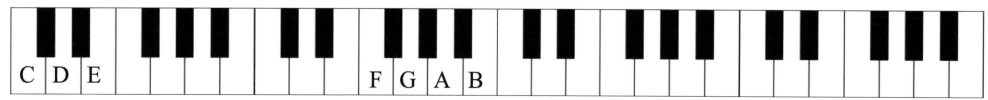

1. Write the names of the keys as shown.　　　2. Find and play these notes on your keyboard.

Teacher's part

Sway away

LONDON CALLING!

4

PLAYING ON BLACK KEYS

This tune can be taught by rote.

 *Top Tip!*

Find the keys with
your eyes first, then
'land' on them
with your fingers!

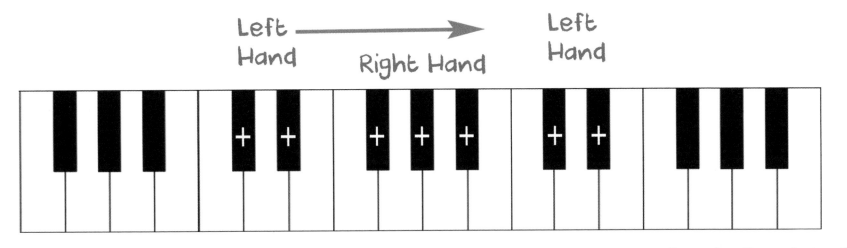

LONDON CALLING!

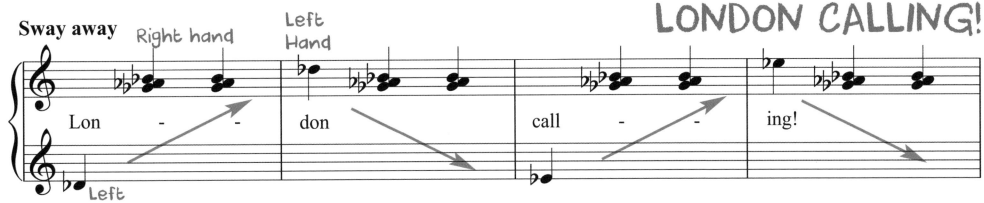

Sway away

Lon - - don — call - - ing!

Lon - - don

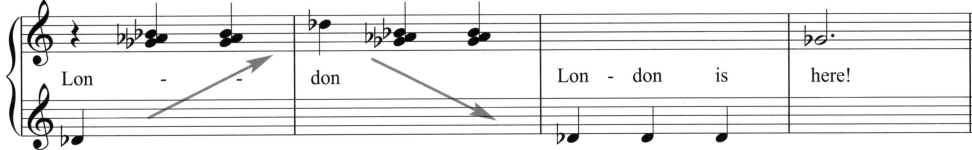

Lon - don is here!

Student's part

5

THE MUSIC ALPHABET

consists of seven notes:

A B C D E F G

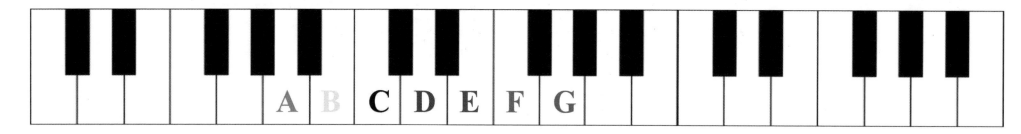

1. Write in the letter names of all white keys.

2. Find and play these notes on your keyboard.

ROYAL GUARD

March

Teacher's part

6

SAY HELLO TO MIDDLE C!

⊕ *Top Tip!*

Try to play this tune with your
right hand and then with your left hand.
You can also play it with any finger.

1. ON THE PIANO:
It is in the middle of your keyboard next to the two black keys.

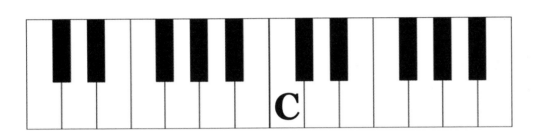

2. IN THE MUSIC SCORE:
It is below the stave on the extra line.

ROYAL GUARD

March

Guards are march-ing   one, two, three, four,   crowd is watch-ing   one, two, three, four.

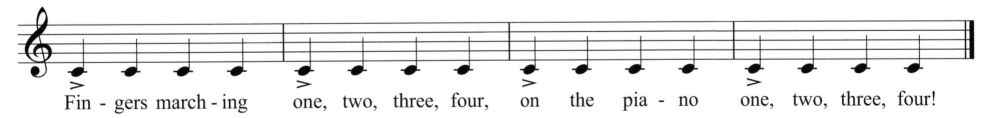

Fin - gers march - ing   one, two, three, four,   on   the   pia - no   one, two, three, four!

Student's part

THE GRAND STAFF

is formed of two staves.

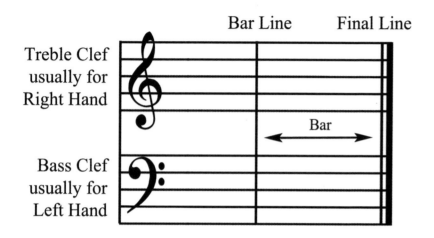

Treble Clef usually for Right Hand

Bass Clef usually for Left Hand

Bar Line   Final Line

Bar

TIME VALUE

indicates the duration of notes.

QUARTER note or CROTCHET
Say TA or STEP
Count one beat

HALF note or MINIM
Say TA-A or STA-AY
Count two beats

TV STATION BBC

Merrily

Teacher's part

NEW NOTE – B

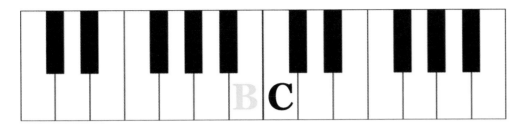

🇬🇧 Top Tip!

Clap the rhythm before playing the tune for the first time!

TV STATION BBC

Clapping exercise: say TA and TA-A, or STEP and STA-AY.

TA - TA - TA - TA TA - TA - TA-A TA - TA - TA - TA TA - TA - TA-A

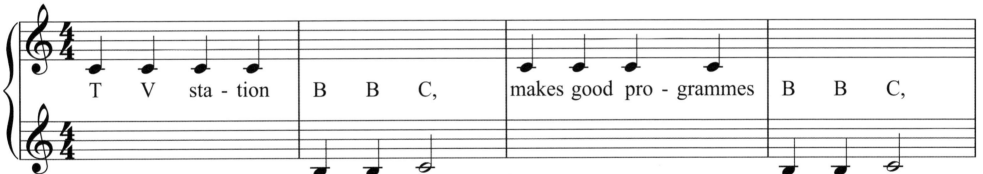

T V sta - tion | B B C, | makes good pro - grammes | B B C,

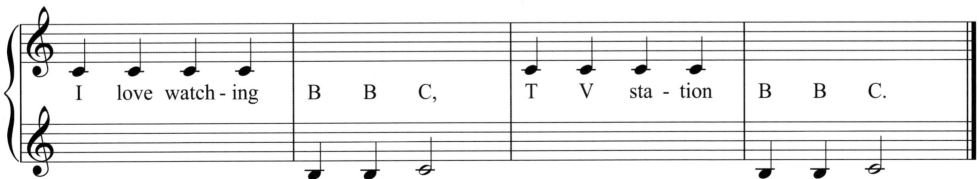

I love watch - ing | B B C, | T V sta - tion | B B C.

Student's part

9

QUIZ Can you score 10 points?

SCORE _____

1. True or false:
this is Middle C. (1)

_____

3. Write the names of the white keys below the three black keys.(4)

2. Write the names of the white keys below the two black keys. (3)

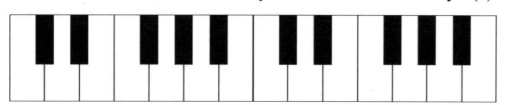

4. True or false:
this is a Treble Clef. (1)

5. How many letters are there
in the music alphabet? (1)

_____   _____

BIRD'S VIEW FROM THE LONDON EYE

Dreamy

Teacher's part

MORE NOTES: D & E

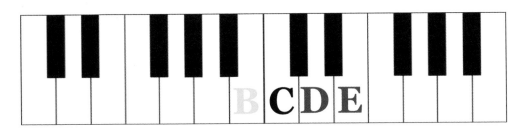

 Top Tip!
You will get a better view
of the piano if you are
sitting up straight.

BIRD'S VIEW FROM THE LONDON EYE

Dreamy

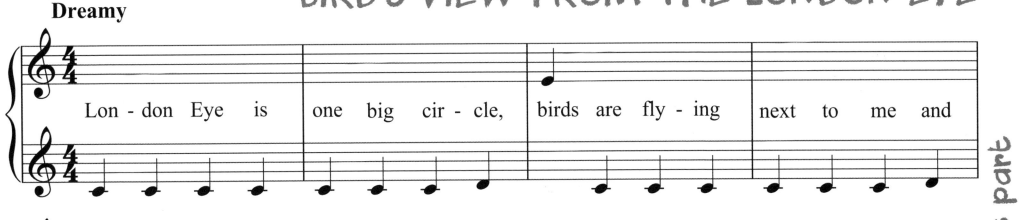

Lon - don Eye is | one big cir - cle, | birds are fly - ing | next to me and

Student's part

mi - llion fa - ces, | thou - sand pla - ces, | birds have best view, | I do too!

11

TIME SIGNATURE

4 The top number tells you how many beats are in the bar/measure.

4 The bottom number tells you that the beat is a crotchet or quarter note.

SPOOKY TOWER

Walking pace

Teacher's part

HEY THERE, THIS IS A!

Clapping exercise: say TA and TA-A, or STEP and STA-AY.

TA - TA - TA-A   TA - TA - TA-A   TA - TA - TA-A   TA - TA - TA-A

WHOLE bar rest

SPOOKY TOWER

Walking pace

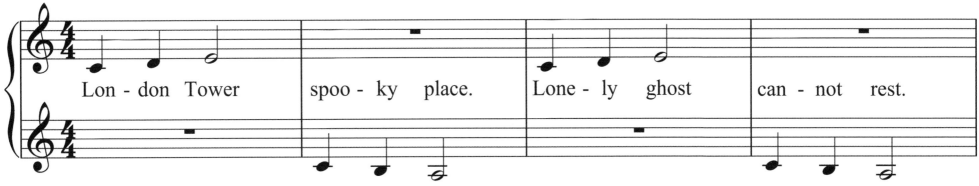

Lon - don Tower   spoo - ky place.   Lone - ly ghost   can - not rest.

Walk - ing slow   in the dark.   Si - lent steps   lone - ly heart.

Student's part

13

FUN ACTIVITY

Spot and circle ten differences
between the two pictures of
Nerdy Cat and score ten points.

CATS & DOGS

Lively

Illustration by Nathalie Chabelnik-Wood

NEW NOTE - F

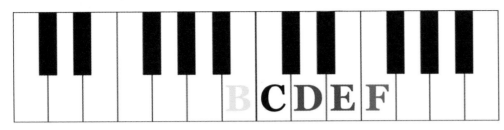

Top Tip!
Aim with your fingertip to land on the key.

INTRODUCING STACCATO

A dot over a note, means to play it short - STACCATO. Keep your wrists flexible and bounce off the key like on a trampoline.

Clapping exercise: say TA and TA-A, or STEP and STA-AY.

TA - TA - TA-A   TA - TA - TA-A   TA - TA - TA - TA   TA - TA - TA-A

CATS & DOGS

Lively

Cats and dogs,   cats and dogs!   It is rain - ing   cats and dogs!

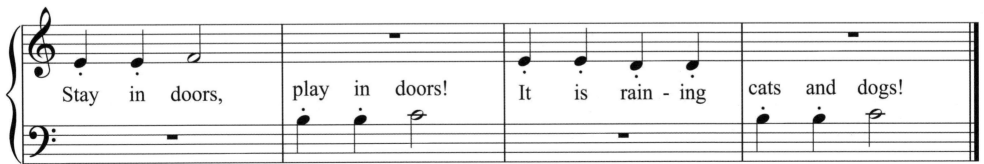

Stay in doors,   play in doors!   It is rain - ing   cats and dogs!

Student's part

15

CROTCHET | QUARTER NOTE REST

For each note time value there is a symbol for silence. We call it a REST.

𝄽 Quarter or Crotchet REST

♩ Quarter or Crotchet NOTE

Let's draw a REST:

Let's draw a NOTE:

1. 2. 3. 1. 2. 3.

Swing

SWINGING BEN

MEET F & G

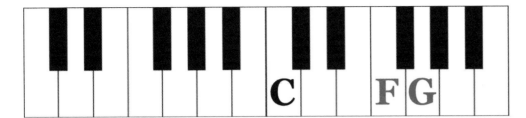

TA - TA - TA - TA   TA - TA - TA - TA   TA - SA - TA - SA   TA - TA - TA - SA

SWINGING BEN

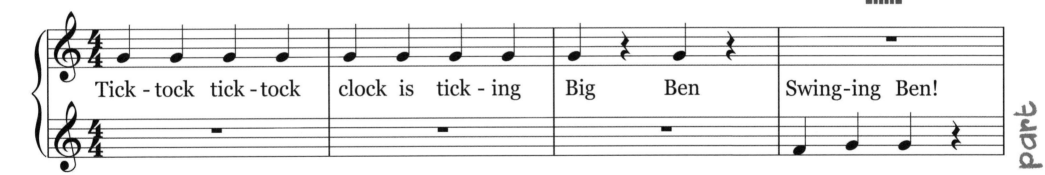

Tick - tock tick - tock | clock is tick - ing | Big   Ben | Swing-ing Ben!

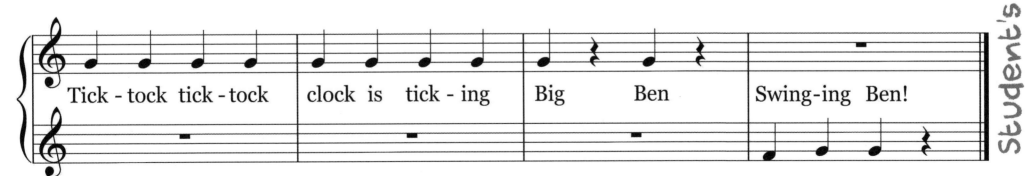

Tick - tock tick - tock | clock is tick - ing | Big   Ben | Swing-ing Ben!

Student's part

17

HOW TO COUNT

Top Tip!
Counting is like
eating greens - it's good for you!

♩ QUARTER NOTE or CROTCHET
Play any key on the piano and say ONE.
The length of time it took for you to say ONE is the time value of that note.

♩ HALF NOTE or MINIM
Play the same key and count ONE - TWO.
The length of time it took for you to say ONE - TWO is the time value of that note.

TEA AT FIVE, SHARP!

F SHARP!

- makes a note higher, go up to the next black key.
- makes all F notes into F sharps in the same bar/measure.

 **Top Tip!**

is a sharp not a hashtag!

 **Fab Fact**

It is thought that the Afternoon Tea tradition was established in the 18th Century by Anne, Duchess of Bedford.

1 2 3 4   1 2 3 4   1 2 3 4   1 2 3 4
TA-TA-TA-A   TA-TA-TA-A   TA-TA-TA-TA   TA-TA-TA-A

TEA AT FIVE, SHARP!

Five o' clock, | time for tea! | Don't be late it's | time for tea!

Sharp! Sharp! | Five o' clock! | Sharp! Sharp! | Time for tea!

Student's part

The idea for this tune was suggested by Sue Parker and Steve Lee (UK).

19

NOTES – C, F, G IN BASS CLEF

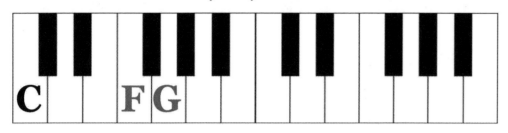

Just for fun, circle these notes with coloured pencils in your score.

Repeat Sign
means play again!

🇬🇧 **Top Tip!**
8vb below the notes
means to play
an octave lower.

DOUBLE-DECKER BASS

twelve bar blues

Groovy

Student's part

BASS CLEF

is for the lower notes on the keyboard.

🇬🇧 **Fab Fact**

In 1941, Miss Phyllis Thompson became the first woman licensed to drive a double-deck vehicle in England.

Let's draw!

1.　　　　2.　　　　3.

Teacher's part
DOUBLE-DECKER BASS

Groovy

8

Teacher's part

NEW NOTES: E, F, G, A IN BASS CLEF

 **Fab Fact**

The present cathedral was designed by Sir Christopher Wren and rebuilt after the Great Fire of London in 1666.

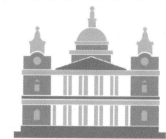

MORNING AT ST PAUL'S

NEW TIME VALUE –
WHOLE NOTE OR SEMIBREVE

⊕ **Top Tip**
Do not ever - under
any circumstances - QUIT!

WHOLE note or SEMIBREVE
O Say TA-A-A-A or SLE-E-E-EP
Count four beats

HOW TO COUNT

Play any key on the piano and say ONE-TWO-THREE-FOUR.
The length of time it took for you to say it, is the time value of that note.

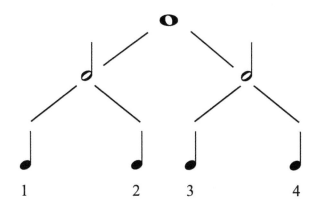

Teacher's part
MORNING AT ST PAUL'S

Walking pace - Andante

pp

23

Teacher's part

NEW TIME VALUE

Let's draw!

♪ EIGHTH note or QUAVER
Say TI or RUN
Count half beat

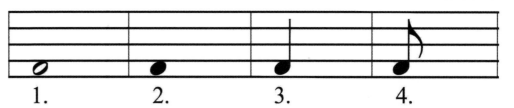

1.   2.   3.   4.

GREAT DETECTIVE

twelve bar blues

With a swagger

b - makes all E notes into E flats in the same bar/measure.

TA - TA - TI-TI - SA   TA - TA - TI-TI - SA

GREAT DETECTIVE
twelve bar blues

With a swagger

Great de - tec - tive   Bob - by Bro-own!   Guard-ing Lon-don   Bob - by Bro-own!

Great de - tec-tive   Bob - by Bro-own!   Guard-ing Lon-don   Bob - by Bro-own!

Great de - tec - tive   on a look out!   Guard-ing Lon-don   Bob - by Brown!

Student's part

25

NEW TIME VALUE

DOTTED quarter note or crotchet
Say TAI or STEP AND
Count one and a half beats

$$\quad . \ = \quad + \ \ = \quad + \ \ + \quad$$

Top Tip!
A dot placed
after a note
makes it HALF
as long again.

GRAVITY

Rock

pp

Teacher's part

Gravity!

26

ANOTHER A!

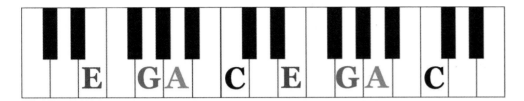

TAI - TI   SA SA   TAI - TI   SA SA   TAI - TI   SA SA   TAI - TI   SA SA

 Top Tip!

8va - - - above the notes means play an octave higher.

Fab Fact

Sir Isaac Newton (1642 - 1727) was a scientist who is credited for discovering gravity.

GRAVITY

Rock

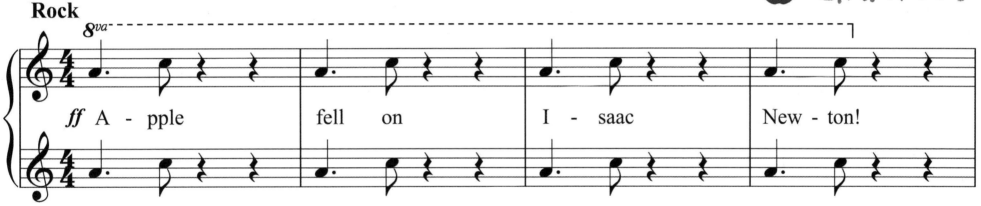

ff A - pple   fell   on   I - saac   New - ton!

Gravity!   Ouch!   Ouch!   Ouch, it's sci - ence!

Student's part

27

INTRODUCING E FLAT

♭ - makes a note lower, go down to the next black key.

BAKER STREET

TAKE THE TUBA
twelve bar blues

The idea for this tune was suggested by Beate Wilmshurst and Andrew Eales (UK).   28

"C" IN THE MIRROR!

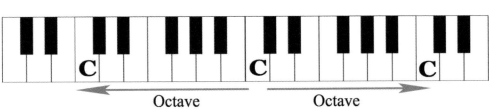

Octave   Octave

TAKE THE TUBA

twelve bar blues

This tune is based on the Blues Scale on C.

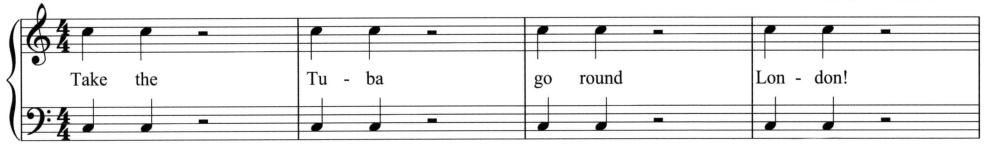

Take   the   Tu - ba   go   round   Lon - don!

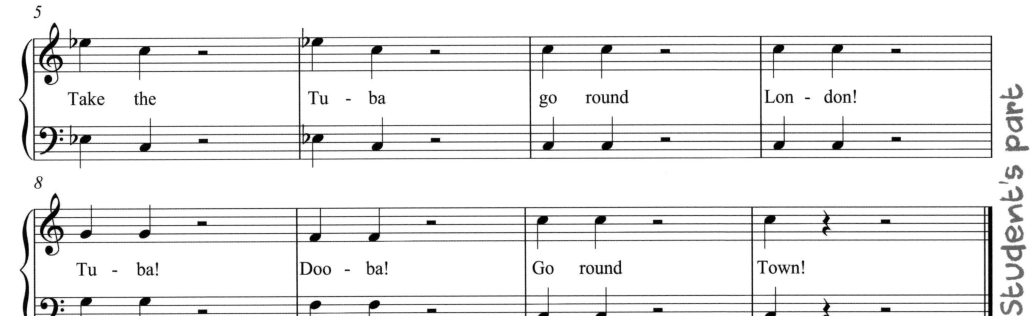

Take   the   Tu - ba   go   round   Lon - don!

Tu - ba!   Doo - ba!   Go   round   Town!

Student's part

Circle the notes with coloured pencils: C Eb F G.

29

LET'S COMPOSE A TUNE!

There are many different ways to compose a song and here is the easiest.

"PIANO TRIP TO LONDON"

1. Say out loud and clap along:

Pia - no trip to Lon - don.

3. Play it on the piano!

2. Using two notes G and D.

Pia - no   trip   to   Lon - don.

"HAPPY SONG, SING ALONG!"

1. Say out loud and clap along:

Hap-py song, sing a - long!

3. Play it on the piano!

2. Choose any notes _____

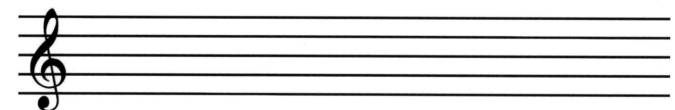

Note to teacher: use a spare sheet if necessary. Ask your student to come up with a phrase too.

MINIM REST & MIDDLE C IN BASS CLEF

Fab Fact

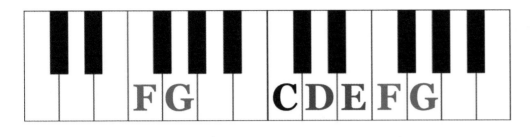

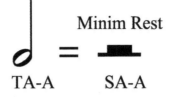

Minim Rest

TA-A   SA-A

Jin - gle bells, jin - gle bells, jin - gle all the way!

After the Illustrated London News (1848) published a drawing of the Royal Family celebrating around a decorated Christmas tree, every home in Britain had a tree bedecked with candles, sweets, fruit and homemade decorations.

JINGLE BELLS IN LONDON

Joyfully

Jin - gle bells, jin - gle bells, jin - gle all the way!

Oh what fun is Lon - don town on fros - ty win - ter day, hey!

Student's solo

LINES & SPACES

Notes are placed on five lines and four spaces. Count from bottom to top.

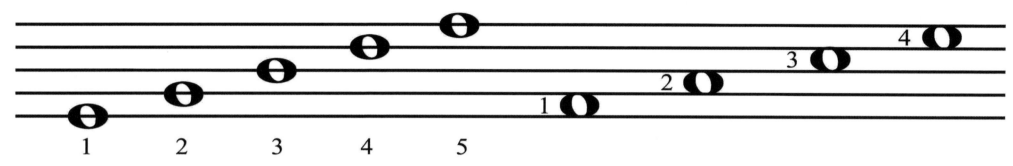

1   2   3   4   5

Draw one note on each line: Draw one note in each space:

L = line and S = space. Draw one note on either line or space:

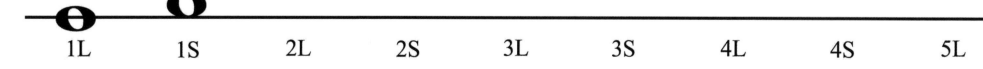

1L   1S   2L   2S   3L   3S   4L   4S   5L

VERY IMPORTANT TIP – the same notes are in different places in Treble and Bass Clefs!

DRAW & COLOUR IN 𝄞

Colour in the notes below according to the colour chart on the right.

A B C D E F G

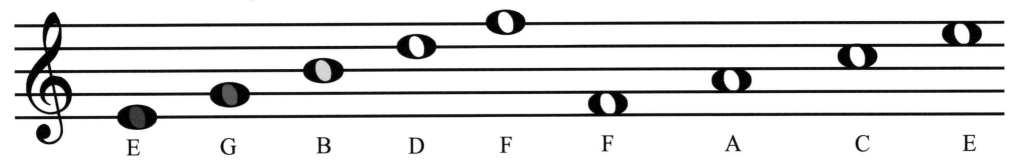

E G B D F F A C E

DRAW & COLOUR IN 𝄢

Colour in the notes below according to the colour chart on the right.

A B C D E F G

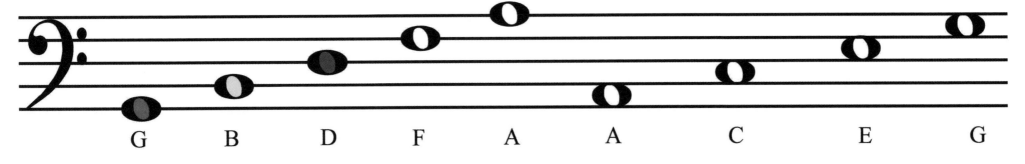

G B D F A A C E G

33

❤ Fab Facts

THE GRAND PIANO

The acoustic piano or pianoforte
has 52 white and 36 black keys.
When you press a key,
a padded hammer strikes the
strings, producing a sound.
The piano was developed
by Bartolomeo Cristofori
in the early 18th Century.

THE DIGITAL PIANO

was designed to imitate the sound of the
acoustic piano using analog circuitry.
The first electronic pianos date from the 1970s.

HEY, DUDE!

Ballade

34

MUSICAL EXPRESSION

These symbols are used to describe expression in music and traditionally we use Italian words.

p   *piano* - play quiet   ◁ - play gradually louder

f   *forte* - play loud   ▷ - play gradually quieter

HEY, DUDE!

Ballade

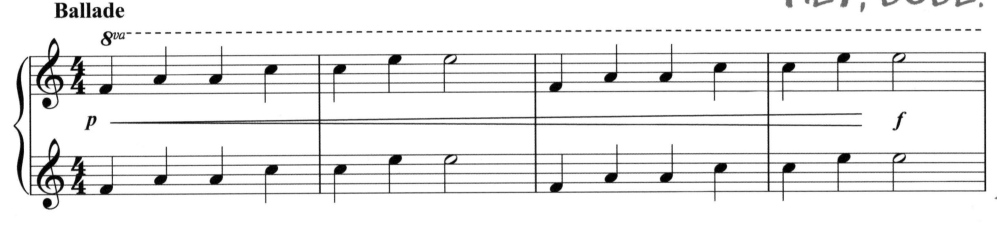

Student's part

35

QUIZ each correct answer scores one point - total score 5 points.

A B C E F G

1. Which note is missing from the music alphabet? _____ (1)

2. What colour is it? _____ (1)

3. Add the missing note to the colour chart above. (1)

4. True or false: this is F _____ (1)

5. It is on the line _____ (1)

AMERICAN IN LONDON

Swing

Teacher's part

Play the first line one more time to end the song.

AMERICAN IN LONDON

With Joy

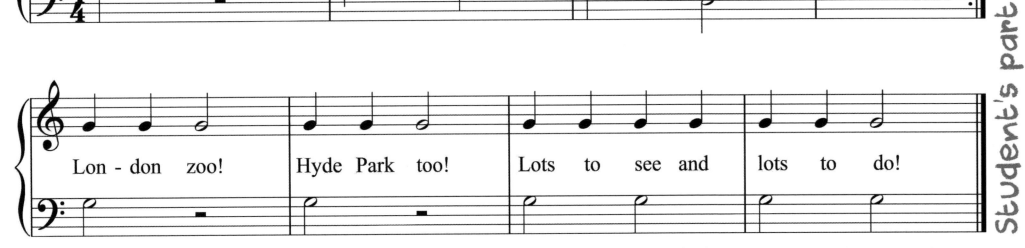

Student's part

Play the first line one more time to end the song.

37

TIME VALUE DIAGRAM

 Top Tip!
Think about it
like sharing a pizza!

Whole	Copy out	**Half**	Copy out	**Quarter**	Copy out	**Eighth**	Copy out

Semibreve   **Minim**   **Crotchet**   **Quaver**

38

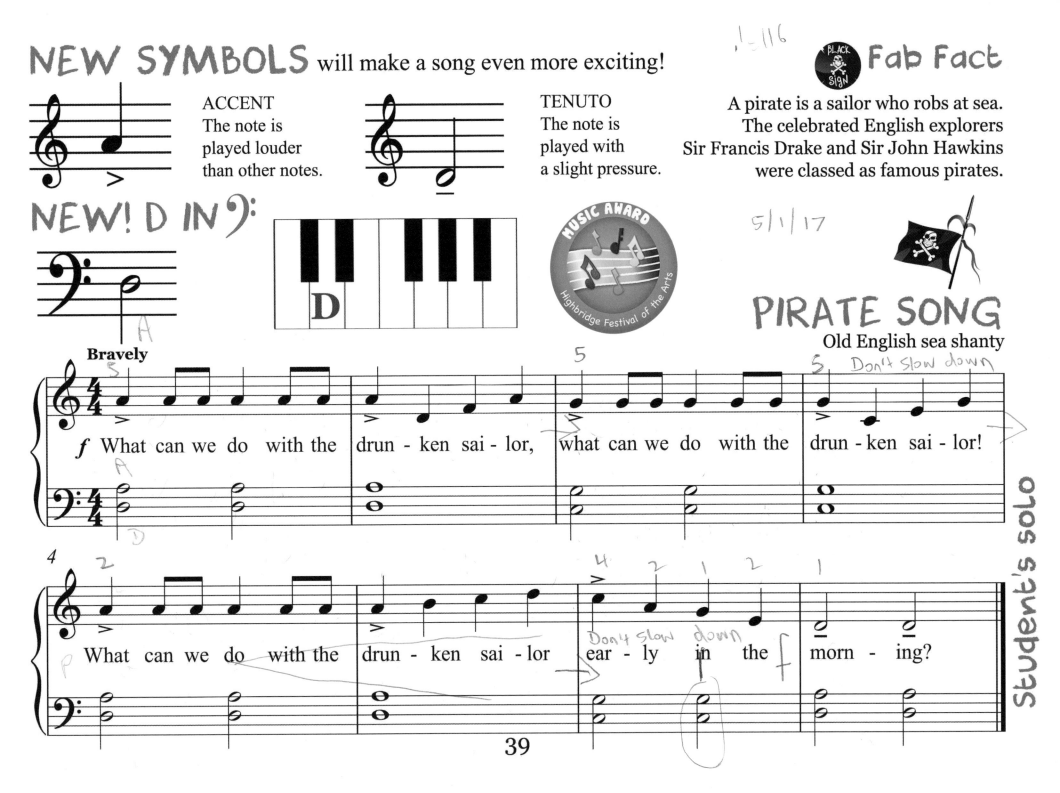

Certificate of Achievement

Name _____

Teacher's Name _____

Date _____

www.elenacobb.com